PRIMAL

BLUE RANGE

DEFEND YOUR DOJO!

Page 13

Page 17

Use these stickers to create your own Power Rangers scenes!

Page 20

Page 29

Page 30

Page 31

Page 53

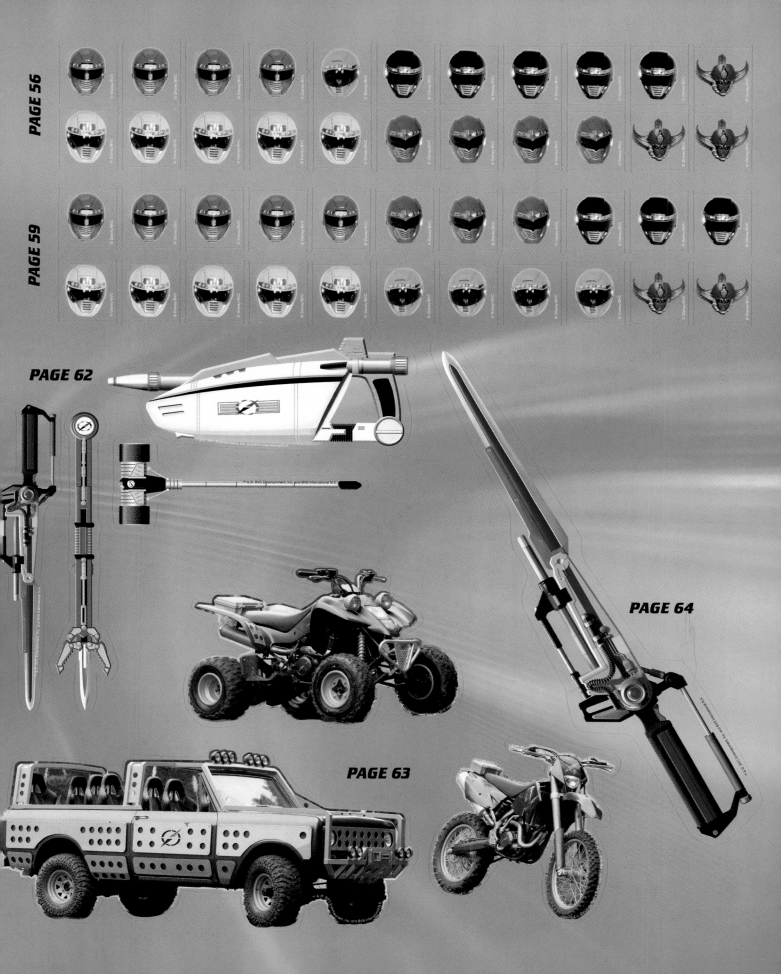

PAGE 56

PAGE 59

PAGE 62

PAGE 64

PAGE 63

Bumper
Sticker Activity

PaRragon
Bath · New York · Singapore · Hong Kong · Cologne · Delhi · Melbourne

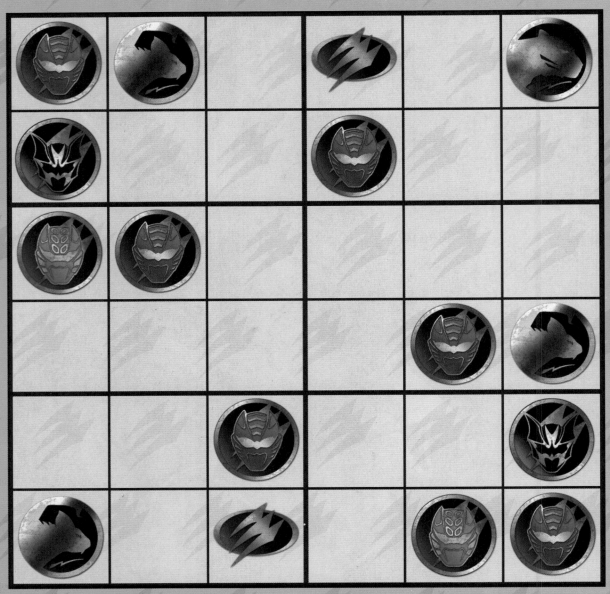

Answer:

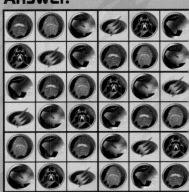

Every row, column and square
must contain each of these images.

Use your Power Rangers stickers to fill in the blank spaces.
Remember, an image cannot appear in the same row,
column or square twice!

ARE YOU TOUGH?
KUNG FU FURY

The Red Ranger is a gifted fighter and risk taker.

The Blue Ranger is the youngest of the Rangers and a great fighter.

JUNGLE JUSTICE

Answer:

Answer:

The Power Ranger helmets are important for protecting each Ranger's true identity.

Can you colour these helmets in the correct colour for each Ranger.

Answer:

Blastin' Baddies!

Use your stickers to make the bottom scene look like the top one.

My answer is:

_____

message to the other Power Rangers.
Help him complete the message
with your stickers, using the code below.

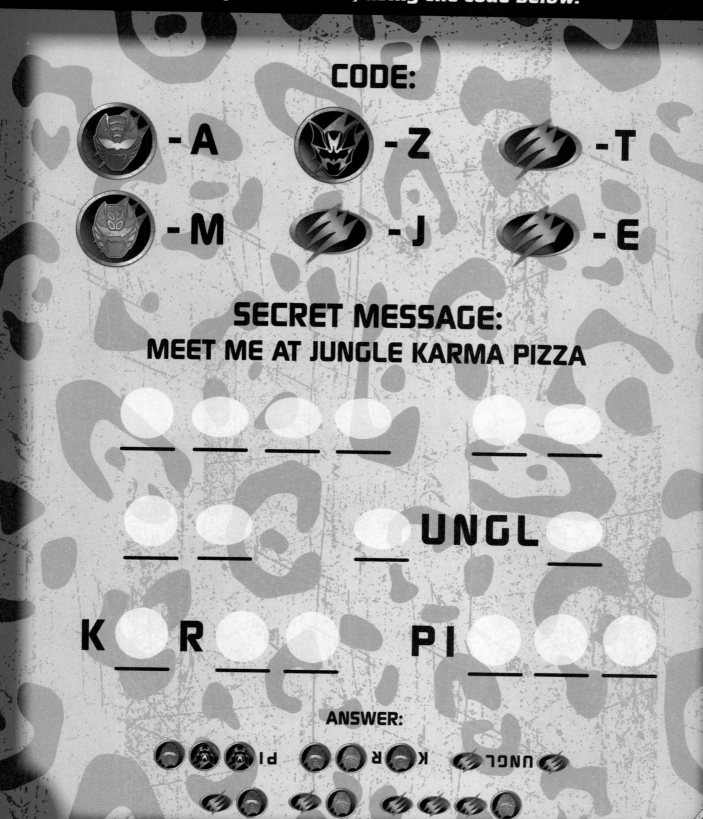

CODE:

◯ - A   ◯ - Z   ⚡ - T

◯ - M   ⚡ - J   ⚡ - E

SECRET MESSAGE:
MEET ME AT JUNGLE KARMA PIZZA

___ ___ ___ ___ ___   ___ ___

___ ___ ___ ___ ___ UNGL◯

K ◯ R ◯ ◯ ◯   PI ◯ ◯ ◯

ANSWER:

17

Follow the trail of clues to work out the mystery identities.

You'll need to unscramble the jumbled words and use your stickers to complete each trail.

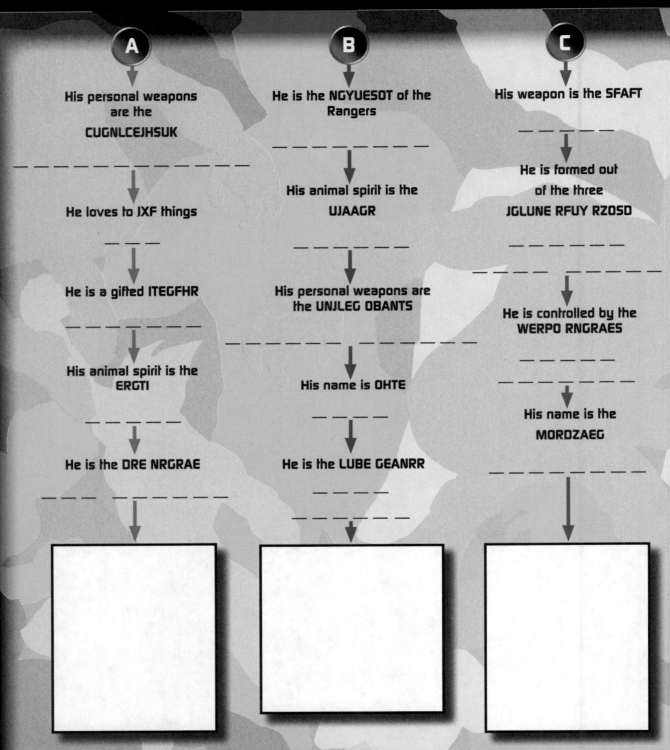

A

His personal weapons are the
CUGNLCEJHSUK

＿ ＿ ＿ ＿ ＿ ＿ ＿ ＿ ＿ ＿ ＿

He loves to JXF things

＿ ＿ ＿

He is a gifted ITEGFHR

＿ ＿ ＿ ＿ ＿ ＿ ＿

His animal spirit is the
ERGTI

＿ ＿ ＿ ＿ ＿

He is the DRE NRGRAE

＿ ＿ ＿ ＿ ＿ ＿ ＿ ＿ ＿

B

He is the NGYUESOT of the Rangers

＿ ＿ ＿ ＿ ＿ ＿ ＿ ＿

His animal spirit is the
UJAAGR

＿ ＿ ＿ ＿ ＿ ＿

His personal weapons are the UNJLEG OBANTS

＿ ＿ ＿ ＿ ＿ ＿ ＿ ＿ ＿ ＿ ＿ ＿

His name is OHTE

＿ ＿ ＿ ＿

He is the LUBE GEANRR

＿ ＿ ＿ ＿ ＿ ＿ ＿ ＿ ＿ ＿

C

His weapon is the SFAFT

＿ ＿ ＿ ＿ ＿

He is formed out of the three
JGLUNE RFUY RZOSD

＿ ＿ ＿ ＿ ＿ ＿ ＿ ＿ ＿ ＿

＿ ＿ ＿ ＿ ＿

He is controlled by the
WERPO RNGRAES

＿ ＿ ＿ ＿ ＿ ＿ ＿ ＿ ＿ ＿ ＿ ＿

His name is the
MORDZAEG

＿ ＿ ＿ ＿ ＿ ＿ ＿ ＿

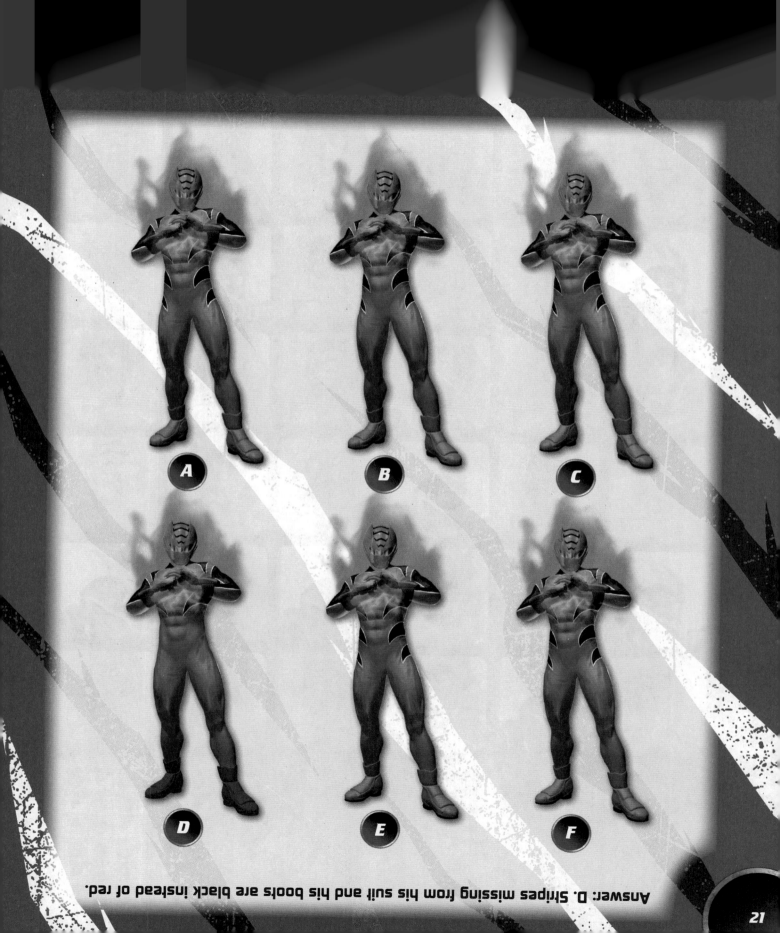

Answer: D. Stripes missing from his suit and his boots are black instead of red.

ANSWER:

22

Mind-Crunching Clues
Solve the clues to find the words that fit in this crossword grid

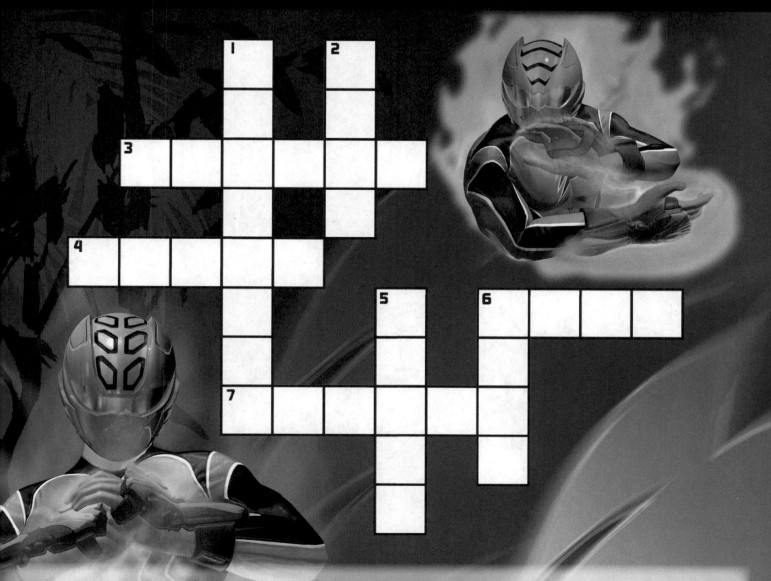

ACROSS

3. The animal spirit of the Blue Ranger (6 letters)
4. Complete the name of the takeaway where the Power Rangers work: "Jungle Karma ———" (5 letters)
6. First name of the delivery person who works at the pizza parlour (4 letters)
7. Evil spirit set on destroying the Earth (6 letters)

DOWN

1. Super fighter, formed out of the Power Rangers' three Zords (8 letters)
2. Complete the name of the secret kung fu clan: "Order of the ———" (4 letters)
5. First name of the Red Ranger (5 letters)
6. A tiny fly with a big mouth (4 letters)

Megazord is the agile martial arts hero formed when all the Jungle Fury Zords are brought together.

Can you count how many times Megazord appears on this page?

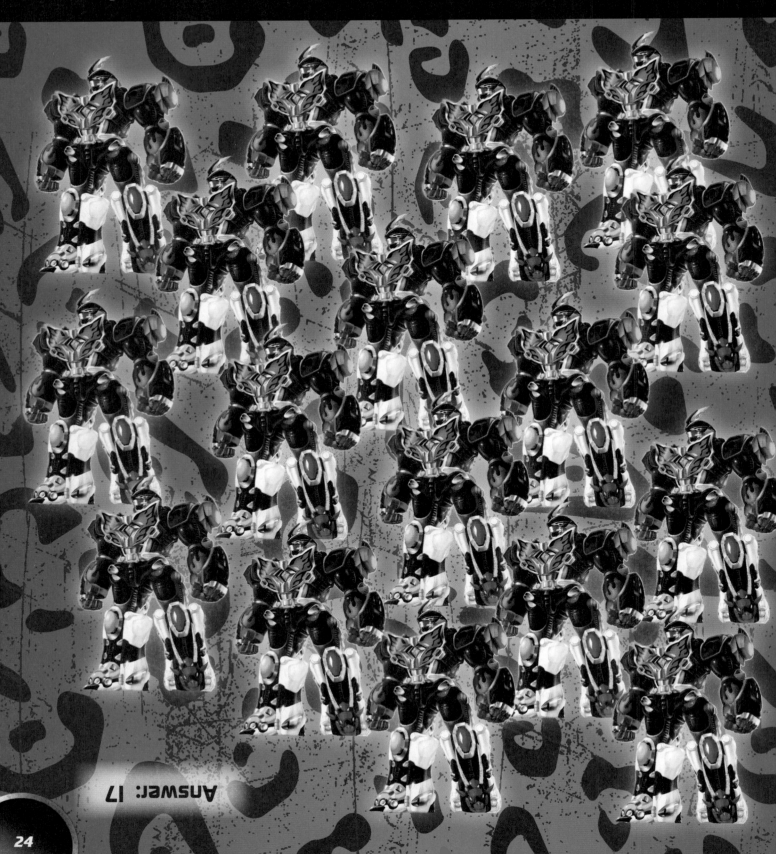

Look up, down, forwards, backwards and diagonally to find the Ranger words in the grid below!

J	U	N	G	L	E	S	T	R	I	K	E
U	Z	R	E	D	O	U	I	Q	J	B	O
N	M	E	G	A	Z	O	R	D	B	I	U
G	D	J	F	U	O	V	I	R	T	G	H
L	Q	A	T	B	E	Z	P	U	D	C	V
E	T	O	I	E	K	R	S	H	F	A	Z
C	E	U	R	S	D	J	L	O	Q	T	R
H	E	Z	A	F	H	R	A	K	E	C	E
U	F	G	N	U	K	I	M	V	B	L	U
C	D	R	G	B	T	E	I	H	O	A	V
K	K	J	E	U	O	R	N	D	Z	S	T
S	F	E	R	Q	R	V	A	J	E	H	F

JUNGLE STRIKE

BIG CAT CLASH

MEGAZORD

JUNGLECHUCKS

DAI SHI

ANIMAL SPIRIT

KUNG FU

RANGER

Answers:

F	H	E	J	A	V	R	Q	R	E	F	S
T	S	Z	D	N	R	O	U	E	J	K	K
V	A	O	H	I	E	T	B	G	R	D	C
U	L	B	V	M	I	K	U	N	G	F	U
E	C	E	K	A	R	H	F	A	Z	E	H
R	T	Q	O	L	J	D	S	R	U	E	C
Z	A	F	H	S	R	K	E	I	O	T	E
V	C	D	U	P	Z	E	B	T	A	Q	L
H	G	T	I	R	V	O	U	F	J	D	G
U	I	B	D	R	O	Z	A	G	E	M	N
O	B	J	Q	I	U	O	D	E	R	Z	U
E	K	I	R	T	S	E	L	G	N	U	J

25

JUNGLE FURY

_____ _____
_____ _____
_____ _____
_____ _____
_____ _____
_____ _____
_____ _____
_____ _____
_____ _____
_____ _____
_____ _____
_____ _____

ANSWERS: Here are just a few words that you
could make using the letters from JUNGLE FURY -
fun, fur, fuel, lunge, jug, gun, glue, run, rug, rule

27

Only one shadow matches the
Blue Ranger exactly.
Can you tell which one?

Answer: 4

Answer:

se your Ranger powers of reasoning and logic to crack this mega-hard sudoku puzzle!

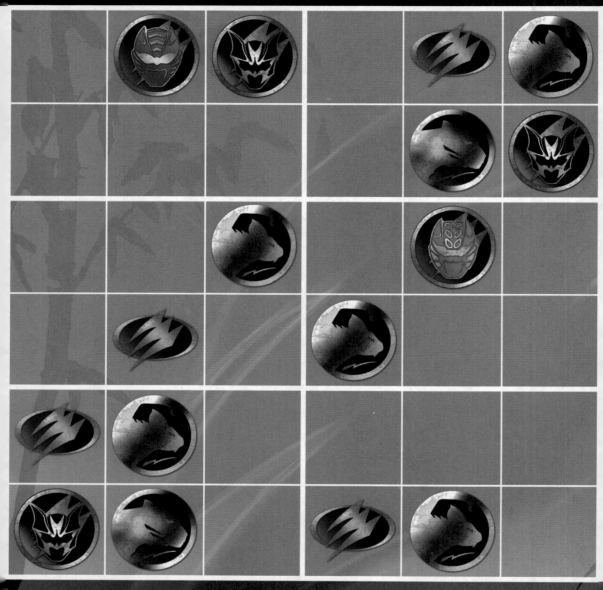

Every row, column and square must contain each of these images.

se your Power Rangers stickers to fill in the blank spaces. Remember, an image cannot appear in the same row, column or square twice!

Answer:

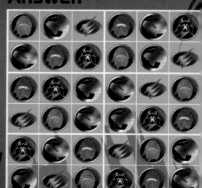

Megazord's Mega-armour!
Use your stickers to complete the missing parts of Megazord's armour.

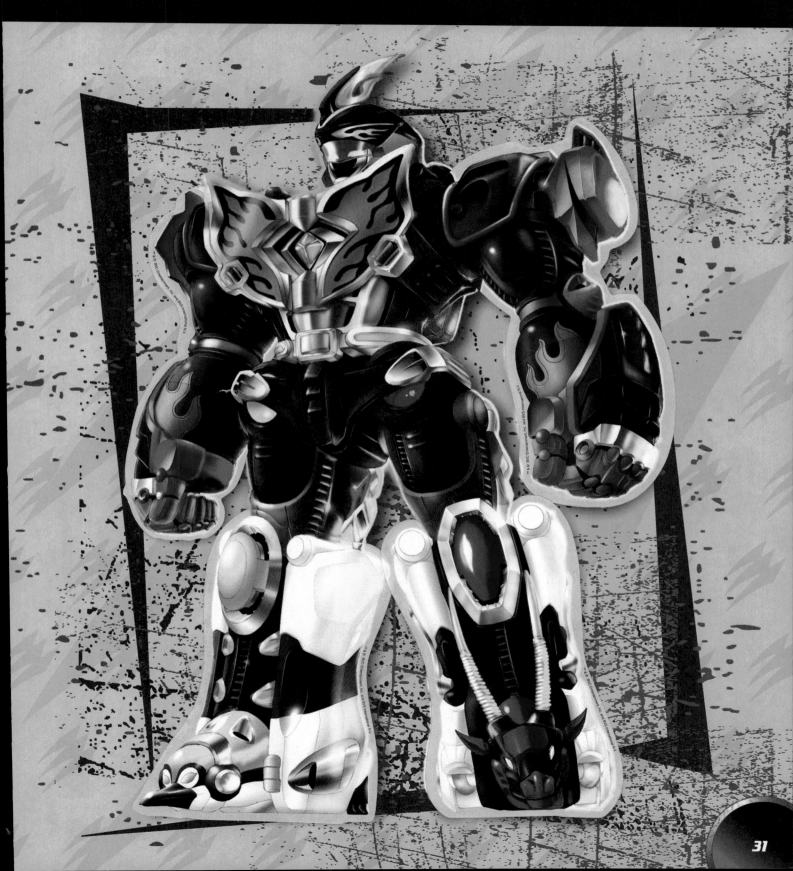

OPERATION OVERDRIVE

POWER RANGERS
OPERATION OVERDRIVE

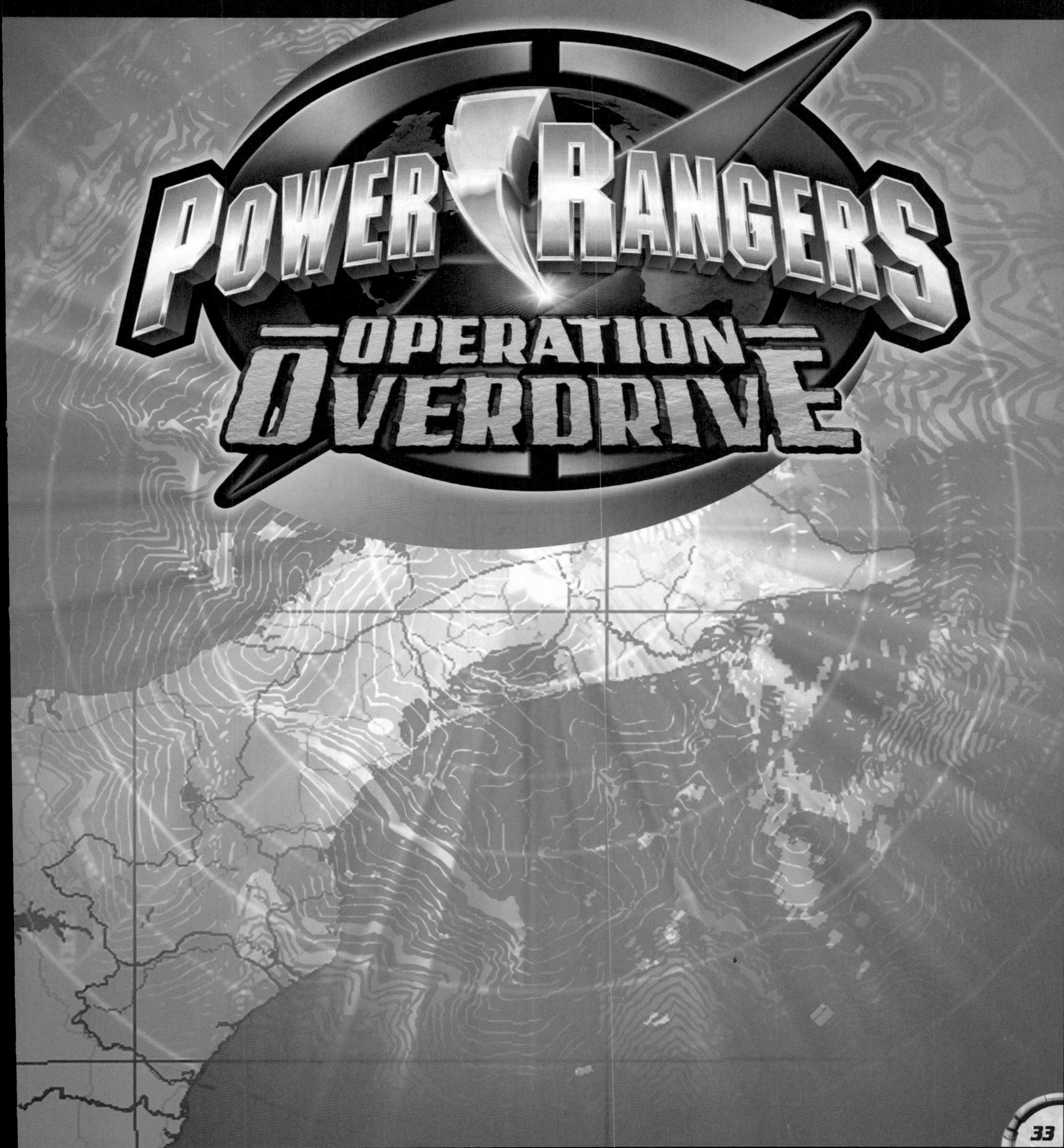

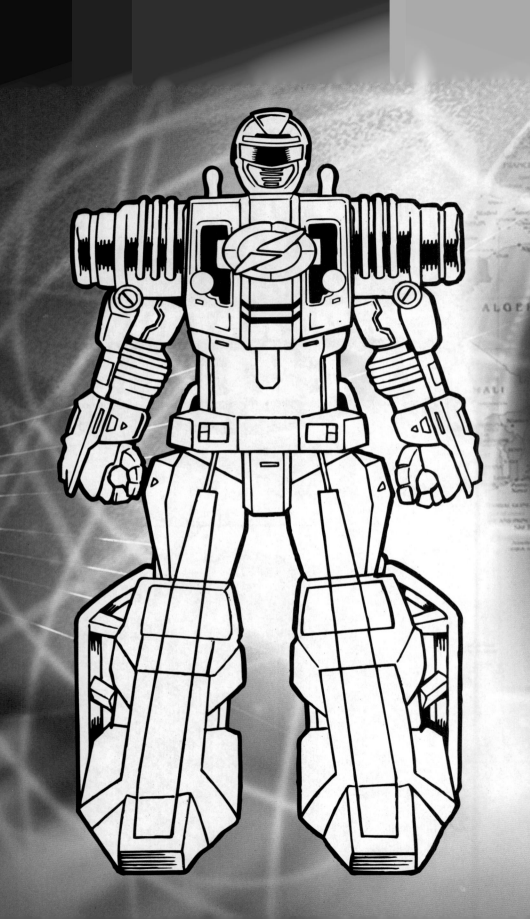

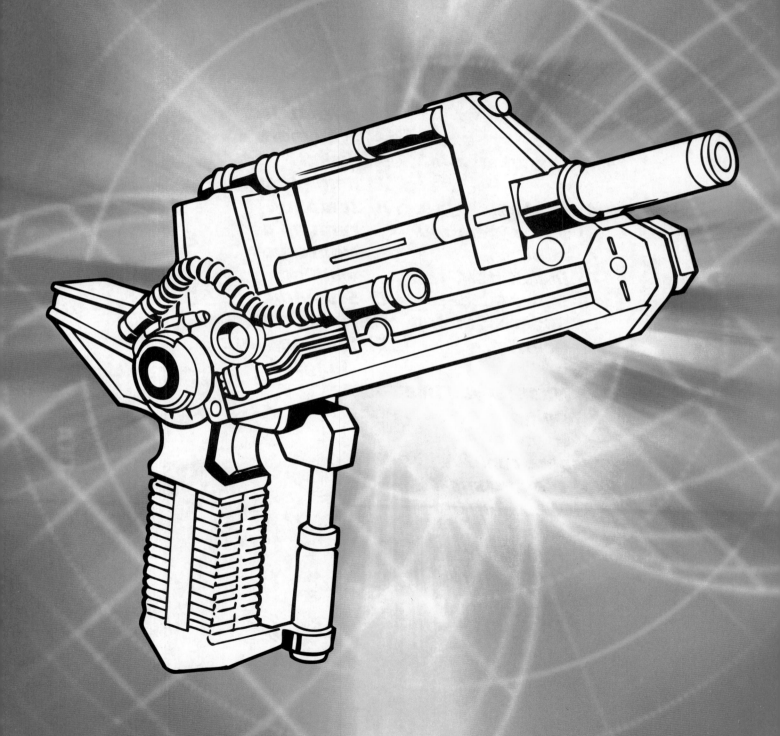

Which Operation Overdrive Power Ranger are you?
Complete the quiz below to find out!

1 If you could have any super power, what would it be?
A) Super strength.
B) Super jumping ability.
C) Invisibility.
D) Super speed.
E) Super sight and hearing.

2 What do you like doing in your spare time?
A) Playing sports.
B) Watching films.
C) Reading poetry.
D) Building cars and learning about engines.
E) Looking at girls.

3 What are you more skilled at?
A) Being brave.
B) Jumping, running and tightrope-walking.
C) Studying.
D) Fixing things.
E) Breaking into things.

4 **What's your idea of a good adventure?**
A) Being able to be independent and figure things out on your own.
B) Running long distances and jumping into action.
C) Having to decipher riddles and solving puzzles.
D) Building things.
E) Spying on enemies and being secretive.

5 **What's your favourite colour?**
A) red
B) blue
C) pink
D) yellow
E) black

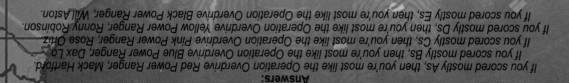

Answers:
If you scored mostly As, then you're most like the Operation Overdrive Red Power Ranger, Mack Hartford.
If you scored mostly Bs, then you're most like the Operation Overdrive Blue Power Ranger, Dax Lo.
If you scored mostly Cs, then you're most like the Operation Overdrive Pink Power Ranger, Rose Ortiz.
If you scored mostly Ds, then you're most like the Operation Overdrive Yellow Power Ranger, Ronny Robinson.
If you scored mostly Es, then you're most like the Operation Overdrive Black Power Ranger, Will Aston.

Our heroes come to the scene to fight!

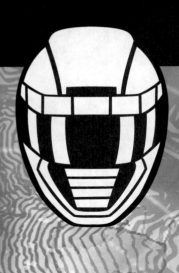

Black Hovertek Cycle

MATCH THE SHADOW

The Power Rangers unite to become the ultimate force for good – the Megazord.
Can you see which shadow matches him exactly?

SHADOW 1

SHADOW 2

SHADOW 3

Answer:

*Many centuries ago, Flurious and his brother, Moltor, tried to steal the Corona Aurora.
But the crown cursed and disfigured them!*

RED MEGAZORD

The Operation Overdrive Power Rangers ride many powerful vehicles that propel them into battle.

**The Blue Ranger is always ready to battle Flurious and Moltor.
He uses his super jumping ability to fight evil.**

Use your expert Ranger knowledge to fill in the gaps in the sentences below.

1) Andrew Hartford is the father of the Red...

2) Spencer is Andrew and Mack's ....

3) The Operation Overdrive Base is located underneath .... Mansion

4) The demon Moltor is the brother of ....

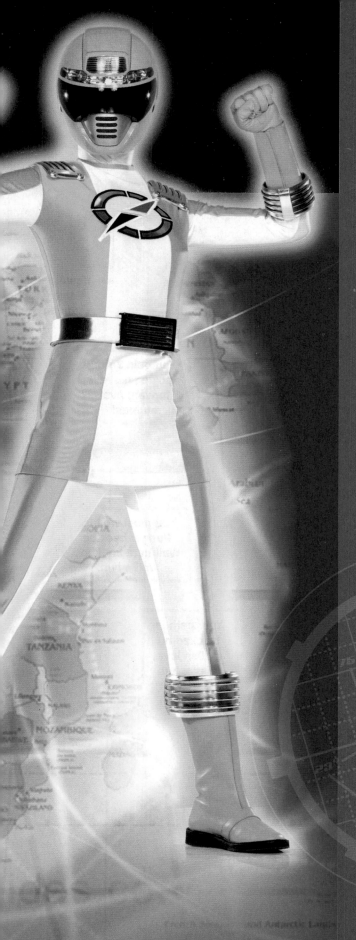

5) Flurious's Lair is covered with snow and ....

6) Moltor's Lair is located inside a molten ....

7) The Corona Aurora is also known as the Crown of the ....

8) The Crown is said to bestow ultimate .... to whoever wears it.

9) Without its ....
the crown is powerless.

BOARDGAME

Create your own Power Ranger counters out of card for this mega-cool game. Take turns with your friends to roll a dice and move around the board. Whoever gets to the end first is the winner!

Beware Kamd **Remain in thi** **square until** **you roll a six**

You gain Zord power, move forward five squares!

You must wait for Ranger back up. Wait here until you roll a two.

Your path is blocked by molten lava, miss a turn.

START

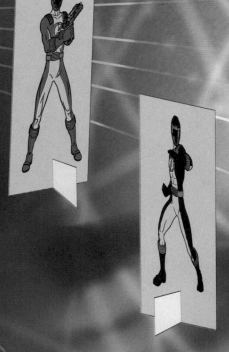

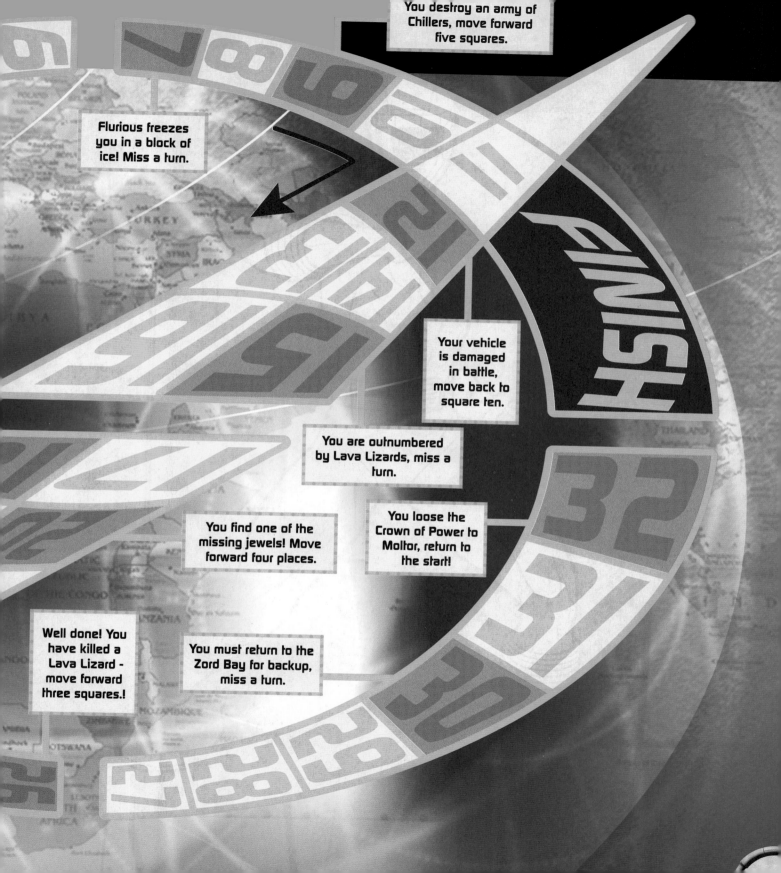

You destroy an army of Chillers, move forward five squares.

Flurious freezes you in a block of ice! Miss a turn.

FINISH

Your vehicle is damaged in battle, move back to square ten.

You are outnumbered by Lava Lizards, miss a turn.

You loose the Crown of Power to Moltor, return to the start!

You find one of the missing jewels! Move forward four places.

Well done! You have killed a Lava Lizard - move forward three squares.!

You must return to the Zord Bay for backup, miss a turn.

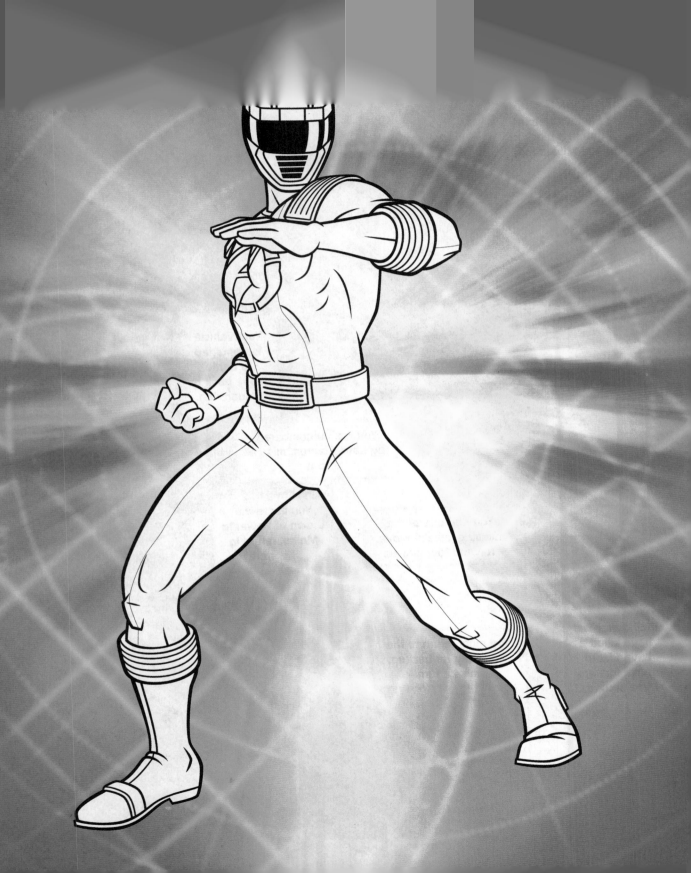

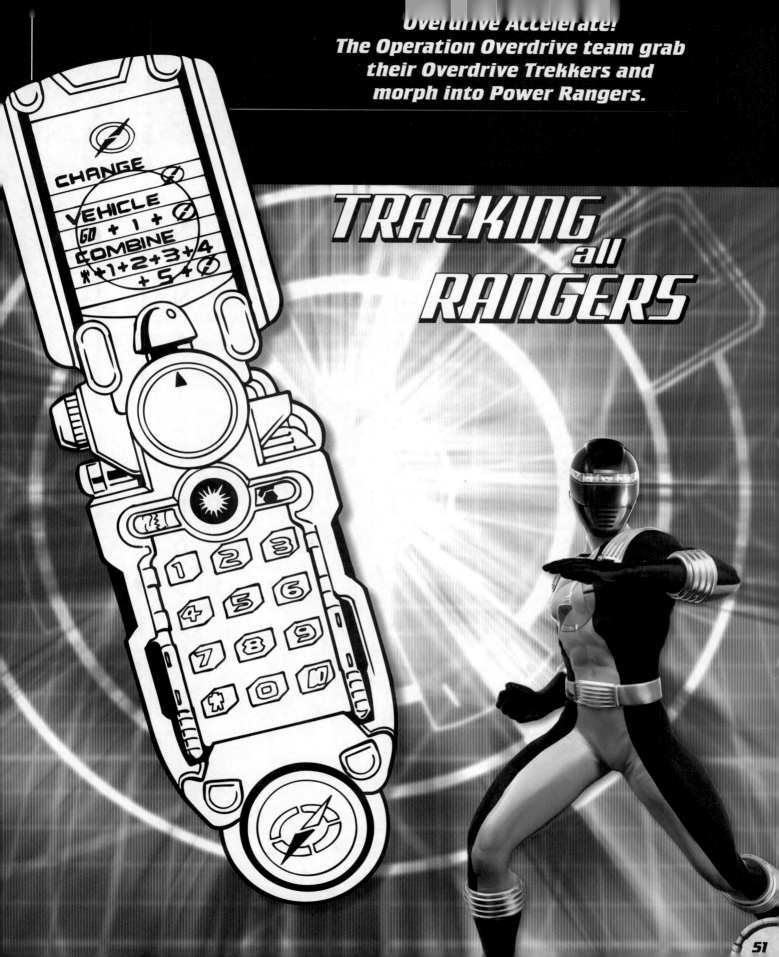

Overdrive Accelerate!
The Operation Overdrive team grab
their Overdrive Trekkers and
morph into Power Rangers.

CHANGE

VEHICLE
GO + 1 +
COMBINE
☆+1+2+3+4
+5+

TRACKING all RANGERS

Look up, down, forwards, backwards and diagonally to find these words in the grid below!

Morpher   Jewel   Invisibility   Zord Bay   Shield   Crown

U	Q	Y	A	R	U	Z	J	W	D	S	I
J	A	R	Z	F	J	X	H	E	F	N	R
H	S	E	X	V	M	C	G	R	V	A	E
G	D	H	S	T	I	S	H	I	E	L	D
T	E	P	W	G	K	V	S	T	G	Q	G
R	R	R	E	B	O	I	F	Y	H	W	J
F	Z	O	R	D	B	A	Y	U	N	E	U
D	G	M	D	I	L	B	D	I	W	D	B
S	H	O	L	E	W	E	J	P	O	S	F
E	V	I	C	Y	P	N	S	O	R	A	K
W	T	M	V	H	M	L	A	L	C	X	S
Y	B	J	F	N	H	K	Q	K	J	C	V

Each Ranger possesses his or her own weapon. Read the weapon profiles, then find the action pose Ranger sticker that goes with each one.

DRIVE LANCE

This is a spear with a retractable blade wielded by the Red Ranger. Using this spear the Red Ranger can do a high-speed slash attack.

Find the sticker that goes here.

DRIVE SLAMMER

The Black Ranger's weapon is a giant hammer that delivers earth-shattering blows.

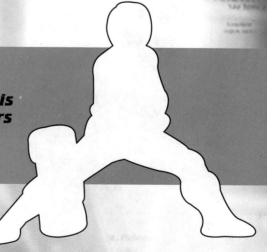

Find the sticker that goes here.

WHICH LINE LEADS TO...

The Black Ranger must use his super powers of sight to lead him to the evil Moltor.
Only then can he battle his enemy and save the world from evil! Which line will lead him to Moltor?

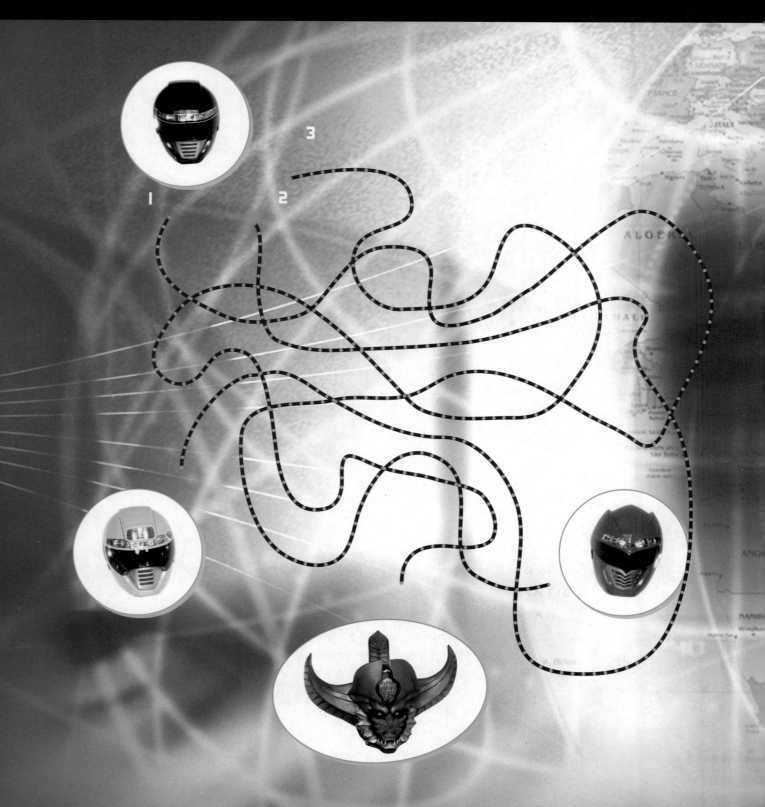

Answer: 3

Help the Rangers crack the code to reveal their special mission. Reading from left to right, top to bottom, cross out the numbers in the grid below and use the remaining letters to fill in the answers.
Clue: There are no zeros in the grid.

The – – – – – – – must track down five long-lost – – – – – – from the – – – – – of – – – Gods. If they fail – – – – Forces will wear the Crown and – – – – will be unstoppable.

R	4	8	A	1	9	N	6	4
2	G	3	6	E	5	1	R	2
S	8	3	4	J	2	E	8	7
5	W	6	3	E	8	4	L	3
2	S	2	5	C	9	5	R	8
1	0	3	4	W	2	6	N	9
7	5	T	2	3	H	2	7	E
5	D	4	6	A	2	7	R	8
K	3	6	E	6	V	5	7	6
4	2	1	3	2	L	9	4	7

Now, unscramble the letters in the coloured boxes to discover where the mission is based:

– – – – –

55

SUDOKU

Use your Ranger powers of reasoning and l ogic to crack this mega-hard sudoku puzzle!

Every row must contain a picture of each of the images below, so must every column and every square. Use your Power Ranger stickers to fill in the missing images in the blank spaces. Remember, an image cannot appear in the same row, column or square twice!

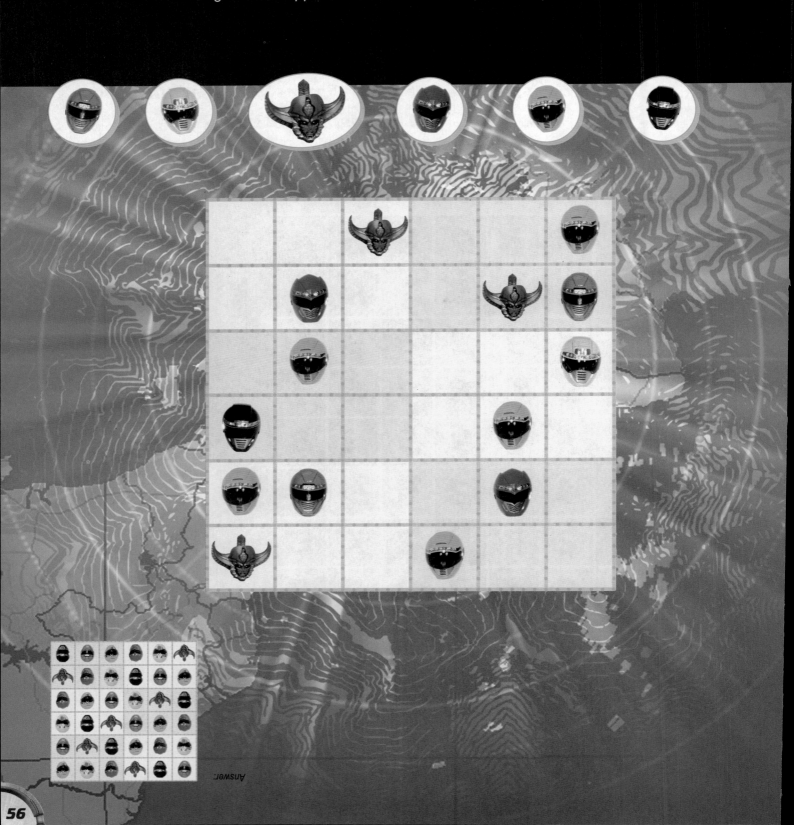

Answer:

_ _ _ _ _ _ _ _ _

_ _ _ _ _ _ _ _ _ _

57

Make as many words as you can using the letters from OPERATION OVERDRIVE.

OPERATION OVERDRIVE

....
....
....
....
....
....
....
....
....
....
....

SUDOKU

Use your Ranger powers of reasoning and logic to crack this mega-hard sudoku puzzle!

Every row must contain a picture of each of the images below. So must every column and every square. Use your Power Ranger stickers to fill in the missing images in the blank spaces. Remember, an image cannot appear in the same row, column or square twice!

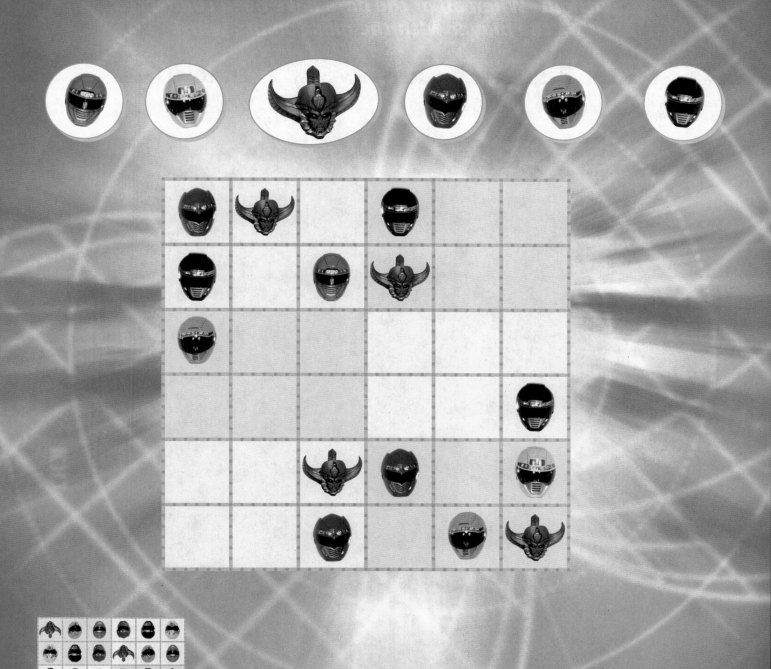

Answer:

59

Take turns with a friend drawing a straight line between any two dots to make a square. When you make a square, put your initials in it and take another turn. Win two points for squares with Power Rangers or symbols in them and one point for squares without. When all of the dots have been connected, the player with the most points wins!

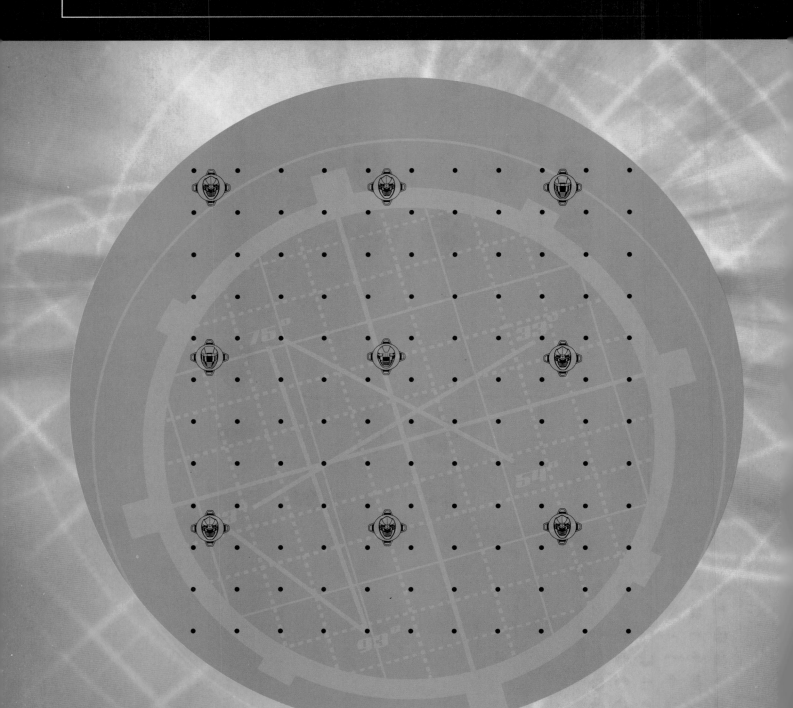

Look up, down, forwards, backwards and diagonally to find the villainous words in the grid below!

I	K	X	M	S	C	S	A	S	X	Q	L
N	L	C	O	D	V	R	S	D	C	A	A
F	Z	V	L	F	B	E	D	F	V	Y	S
E	F	B	T	G	N	L	F	A	V	U	D
R	L	N	O	H	M	L	L	G	B	R	F
N	U	M	R	J	Q	I	G	H	N	O	G
O	R	Q	U	K	Z	H	H	J	M	D	H
D	I	E	I	A	E	C	J	K	Q	M	J
F	O	R	R	L	R	Q	K	L	E	A	K
G	U	D	O	Z	T	Q	L	L	R	K	L
H	S	T	P	I	C	E	D	E	N	I	Z
J	Q	Y	A	X	Y	Q	A	Z	T	O	X

INFERNO
MOLTOR
FLURIOUS
LAVA LIZARDS

CHILLERS
ICE DEN
KAMDOR

NAME THE WEAPON

The Power Rangers have many weapons, which they use to fight evil.
Use your stickers to match the correct weapons to these names.

1) Drive Geyser

2) Drive Slammer

3) Drive Defender

4) Drive Lance

FURY